EXPLORING THE UNDERCLIFFS

Donald Campbell

The Axmouth to Lyme Regis National Nature Reserve

A 50th Anniversary Guide

A Coastal Publishing Book

Written by Donald Campbell
Project Editor Professor Denys Brunsden
Design Jonathan Lewis
Production Peter Sills

First Published in Great Britain 2006
Reprinted 2010
By Coastal Publishing
The Studio, Puddletown Road
Wareham, Dorset BH20 6AE

www.coastalpublishing.co.uk
A Sillson Company

Funded by English Nature, Heritage Lottery Fund and the Jurassic Coast Trust.

A fund-raising Trust has been established to hold the proceeds of this publication, and other officially recognised products about the World Heritage Site. Funds will be used to support the conservation and education programme for the site.

A (CIP) Cataloguing in Production record is available from the British Library

ISBN 0-9544845-2-5

Acknowledgements

This booklet arose from meetings with Prof. Denys Brunsden (World Heritage Trust) and Albert Knott (English Nature). Many thanks to both of them and to those who commented so usefully on parts of the text; these include Keith Moore, Peter Grainger, Colin Dawes and Roger and Kath Critchard, while Tim Badman made many useful suggestions. Jo Draper and Mike Cawte, like all at the Lyme Regis Museum, are always helpful as are the Allhusen family who allow me convenient access to the Undercliffs. I am grateful for permission to quote from the work of Richard Fortey, John Fowles, Elaine Franks and Norman Moore. Two very special thank you's go to Sarah Miller who has again converted my dreadful scrawl into an organised and coherent form, and to Norman Barns who introduced me to many of the secrets of the Reserve.

Image acknowledgements

My special thanks to Nigel Cozens of Lymelight Books for making available some of his wide range of prints (pages Front cover,4,5,18-22,24,27,28) and to Colin Varndell for supplying images (43,44,46,47,51,56,57,58,60) by special request. The World Heritage Coast Trust (mapping derived from OS data Licence Number 100045284 page 6,7) Many others have helped including Keith Moore (10,11), Richard Edmonds (14,15) for his unique Undercliffs panorama also page (33), West Dorset District Council (17,49), Val Baker (26,38), Jeremy Smith (54), The Victoria and Albert Museum, London (34,35), Natural History Museum, London (30,31,32), Roderick Gordon and Diana Harmer Collection (31), Roger Critchard (38,39), Roger Key (40,47,49,50), Robin Williams (43,48), Elaine Franks (45, 45), Peter Sills (8,41,52,53), Chris Pamplin (13), Peter Grainger (17), Phil Parr (49), Andy Callow (50), Jonathan Lewis (16), and Tom Jenkyn (50,55,59). Aerial photograph on page 37 © UKP Licence No. UKP2005/02. My wife, Nicky, made the lithograph on page 36 available from her Peek Estate archive. The other images on pages (9,10,12,39,40,42,48,53,57,61,62,63,64) are from my private collection. Whilst every endeavour has been made to ascertain the copyright owners, some of the images have remained elusive, for this we apologise.

CONTENTS

'There are surely on occasions other values in the balance besides the acquisition of new knowledge or university research. Public education is one. Another, if you will excuse me using such an unscientific word, is what I would call poetic – imparting a sense, however small, of the age and complexity of existence, both animate and inanimate, on this planet.'

John Fowles at the British Association for the Advancement of Science meeting in Liverpool, September 1982.

This guide is dedicated to the memory of Muriel Arber who loved the Undercliff and who provided perceptive accounts of the geomorphology.

The Axmouth to Lyme Regis Undercliffs National Nature Reserve is the finest 'wilderness' area in Great Britain. It is the only reserve in the world whose raison d'être is landslides and the complex habitats that develop on moving land. It makes a dynamic interface between the land, atmosphere and ocean. The foreshore is wide, constantly changing in character and rarely visited by people. The cliffs are spectacular but covered by the most magnificent trees, ivy and rich undergrowth.

It is easy to get lost here. To some it is wet, overhung, claustrophobic and frightening. To others it is romantic, intriguing and beautiful. Topophobia and topophilia are easy companions here. It is the site of the first scientific study of landslides. It has been one of my sources of inspiration. This wonderful book introduces us to some of its mysteries including a little of the rich human history, and the people who made it. The World Heritage Coast Trust congratulates English Nature, the land owners and voluntary wardens for their vision and custodianship over the last 50 years. We thank Donald Campbell for his commitment to the conservation of this unique area.

Professor Denys Brunsden

L. E. Reed - View of the principal chasm showing the fractured turnip field.

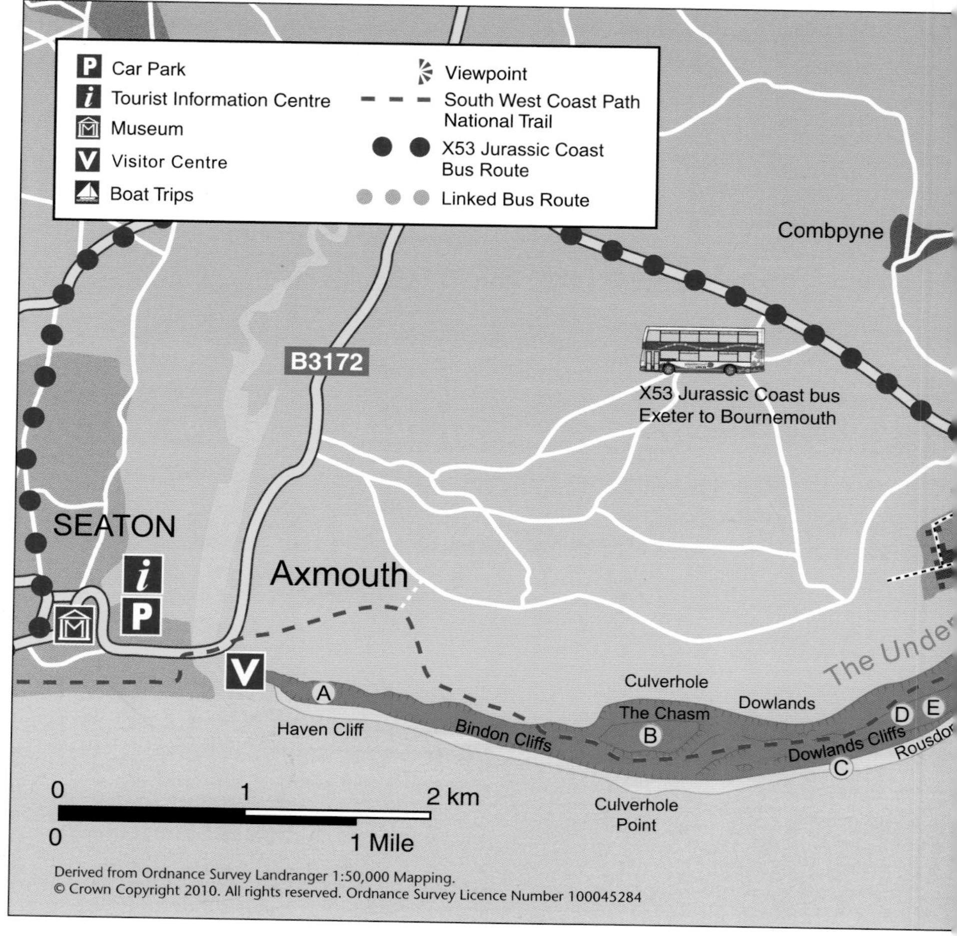

The Axmouth to Lyme Regis Undercliffs National Nature Reserve

The 335 hectares of the Undercliffs Site of Special Scientific Interest is one of the largest active coastal landslide systems in Western Europe. The National Nature Reserve which makes up 91% of this area is the only British reserve holding the entire range of important features characteristic of this type of environment. It is an area of wild woodland and scrub with chalk plateaux and impressive cliffs.

In addition to its status within the Jurassic Coast World Heritage Site, it is part of the Sidmouth to West Bay Special Area of Conservation and forms the south eastern part of the East Devon Area of Outstanding Natural Beauty. This guide tells you more of its outstanding interest in terms of geology, geomorphology, ecology and landscape.

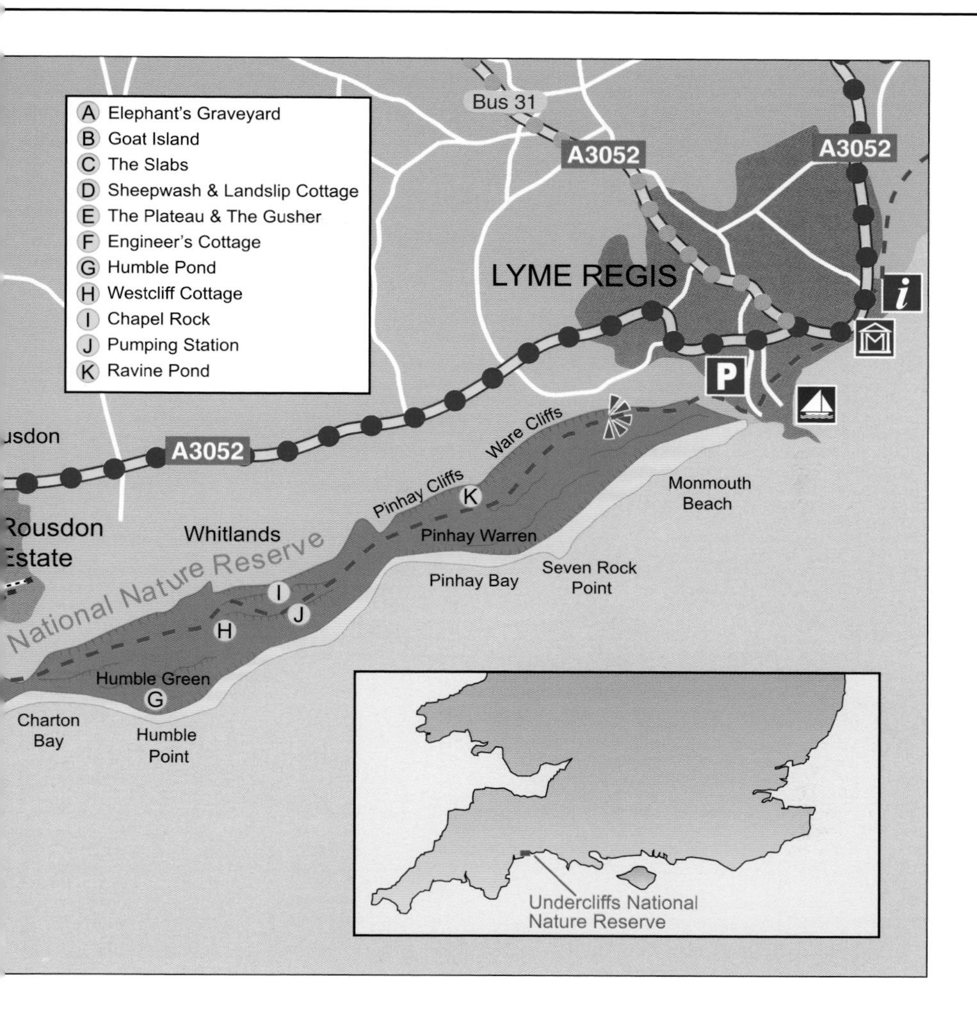

The area marks the transition from the Triassic rocks of East Devon, particularly evident at Ladram Bay and Sidmouth, and the Jurassic rocks, with their fossil rich sites as at Lyme Regis and Charmouth. With overlying Cretaceous Chalk and Upper Greensand, the Undercliffs contain rocks from the three geological periods found within the first natural World Heritage Site in England. The Sidmouth to West Bay coastline is also internationally important for the mosaic of vegetation types that occur on its soft cliffs. Within the East Devon Area of Outstanding Natural Beauty these coastal cliffs and woodlands contrast with pebble bed heaths, river valleys and Greensand ridges.

Please read the safety advice on page 64/65

World Heritage Status

The purpose of the World Heritage convention of UNESCO is to protect and conserve places of 'outstanding universal value' and to present them to visitors. They may be of natural or cultural value, or both. Each Site has a distinctive character and management plan.

The Dorset and East Devon World Heritage Site is a natural site containing a coastal strip of land, around 95 miles (155 km) in length, lying between the top of the cliffs and the low water mark. It was declared a World Heritage Site by UNESCO on 13th December 2001, as:

> *'An outstanding example representing major stages of the Earth's history, including the record of life, significant ongoing geological processes in the development of landforms, and significant geomorphic or physiographic features.'*

The Site is popularly known as the 'Jurassic Coast' after the best known of the geological periods found within it. The Site includes rocks from the Triassic, Jurassic and Cretaceous Periods. These periods make up the Mesozoic Era of geological time, between 250 and 65 million years ago.

English Nature and National Nature Reserves

National Nature Reserves represent the best examples of natural or semi-natural wildlife habitats and geological sites. They are managed by English Nature and a range of approved organisations. English Nature came into being in April 1991 and among its aims is the enhancement of public awareness of the natural world. The first seven National Nature Reserves were declared on 19th May 1952 and there are now some 200. The Undercliffs Reserve was initially declared on 16th March 1955 and is among the wildest in England. It was made famous by the Great Landslide of 1839 and as the setting of much of the film of 'The French Lieutenants Woman', based on the novel by the late John Fowles.

Albert Knott (centre), Assistant Site Manager, identifying plants on the Plateau.

How the Reserve is managed?

Successive Management Plans have mainly advocated limited intervention, leaving natural processes to shape the landscape. Areas of chalk grassland are actively managed and some introduced species are controlled. Glade creation and pond clearance also takes place. The East Devon District Council Countryside Service manages this part of the South West Coast Path National Trail.

Phil Page, Site Manager, mowing on Goat Island.

Who owns the National Nature Reserve?

Most of the Reserve, like 'Goat Island', the central grassland area (see page 8), is privately owned.

Haven Cliff showing Triassic Mudstones (red) and Cretaceous Chalk (white). The Clay with Flints (orange) at the top of the cliff include Tertiary and Quaternary materials. The Upper Greensand is largely concealed by landslides.

QUAT		x	CLAY-WITH-FLINTS
CRETACEOUS	U.	6c	UPPER CHALK
		6b	MIDDLE CHALK
		6a	CENOMANIAN LST.
	L.	5c	TOP SANDSTONE
		5b	CHERT BEDS
		5a	FOXMOULD/GAULT
LOWER JURASSIC	L. LIAS	g1c	BLACK VEN MARLS
		g1b	SHALES WITH BEEF
		g1a	BLUE LIAS
UPPER TRIASSIC	U. TRIAS	Fg	RHAETIAN
		f6b	GREEN MERCIA MDST.
			RED MERCIA MDST.

HAVENCLIFF
BINDON
R.AXE
5c
Fba
WEST.

A look at the Rocks

The older Triassic and Jurassic rock layers dip gently to the south east, and therefore the rocks exposed on the surface become younger from Axmouth Harbour towards Lyme Regis. The sequence is broken and repeated due to faulting and folding. The diagram below shows how the dipping Triassic and Jurassic rocks are overlain by horizontal, younger Cretaceous rocks. They are separated by a geological feature known as an unconformity, which represents a time gap between the rocks of different ages. Within the Reserve desert sediments, the Triassic Mercia Mudstone, is overlain by the Jurassic Blue Lias, deposited on the sea floor. Later these strata were subject to folding, faulting and extensive erosion. Then the whole area was resubmerged, in one of the great drownings of our islands, leading to the deposition of the Gault and Upper Greensand (shown as Top Sandstone, Chert Beds and Foxmould in the key below) and Chalk. Further uplift, without much distortion, led to the arrangement of strata that we see today. The Triassic and Jurassic rocks are separated from those of the Cretaceous by a period of erosion to produce the unconformity. At the middle of the section, at Rousdon or Charton, the Blue Lias was laid down 200-195 million years ago and the Upper Greensand after a time gap of 100 million years. Therefore most of the Jurassic is missing at this point.

The Upper Greensand contains the mineral glauconite which is green when freshly exposed. When at its most sandy Upper Greensand is known as the Foxmould. The uppermost layer is a soil known as the Clay-with-flints. It is a residue derived from the weathering of Chalk under the sub-tropical conditions of the Tertiary Period.

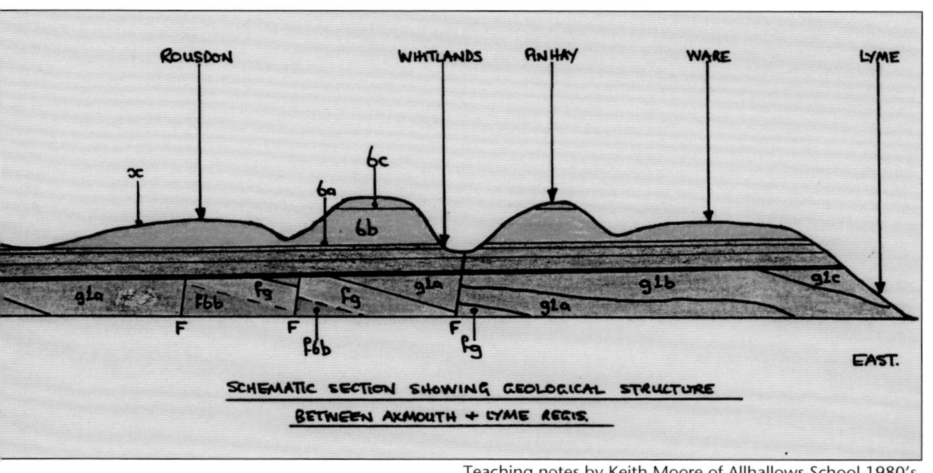

Teaching notes by Keith Moore of Allhallows School 1980's.

Geological Strata

Above the Mercia mudstones at Culverhole Point, Charton Bay and Pinhay Bay, are examples of the youngest Triassic rocks which includes the White Lias.

The appearance of the ammonite *Psiloceras* near the base of the Blue Lias marks the start of the Jurassic period.

The Jurassic Blue Lias is rhythmic in that layers of shales alternate with limestones. Lyme quarrymen were familiar with these layers, which they gave names like Venty, Best Bed, and Rattle. Many famous scientists, gave accounts of the Blue Lias during the 19th century but much of the detail is associated with W. D. Lang a geologist who lived in Charmouth and studied the strata 'inch by inch' between 1923 and 1936.

Blue Lias cliffs in Pinhay Bay.

SYSTEM	STAGE	COMPOSITION
	UPPER CHALK	White chalk with flints
	MIDDLE CHALK	Mainly flint free and gritty
CRETACEOUS	CENOMANIAN LIMESTONE	Abundant fossils
145 – 65 million years ago	UPPER GREENSAND	Glauconitic sandstone above Chert with Foxmould below
Unconformity	GAULT	Sandy clay
	BLACKVEN MARLS	Organic rich mudstones with Birchi limestone
JURASSIC	SHALES WITH BEEF	Mudstones and calcite (beef)
200 – 145 million years ago	BLUE LIAS	Limestones and mudstones
	WHITE LIAS	Pale grey limestones
TRIASSIC	MERCIA MUDSTONES	Soft dark mudstones
250 – 200 million years ago		Grey and green silty mudstones

Stratigraphic column for part of the Mesozoic.

31 THIRD QUICK
30 THIRD QUICK SHALES
29 TOP TAPE
SECOND TAPE
25 TOP COPPER
23 MONGREL
21 SECOND MONGREL
19 SPECKETTY
18
17 THIRD TAPE OR UPPER WHITE BED
16
15 UPPER SKULLS
14
13 IRON LEDGE
12 IRON LEDGE SHALES
11 UNDER COPPER
10
9 UNDER WHITE BED
8
7 LOWER SKULLS
6
5 LOWER VENTY
3 SOFT BED (PIG'S DIRT)
1 BRICK LEDGE
(shales with bands and nodules of limestone)
H91 to H73 thin undulatory lsts and shales (details not shown accurately here)
Reef H72
H70
H68
H67
Reef H66
H64
H62
Reef H60 limestones and shales
H56
Reef H54 grey shelly limestone
shale with five beds of even-bedded limestone
Reef H42
H40 shale with five irregular beds of limestone
Reef H30 compact lst with marly base
five limestones separated by shale (*Triassic-Jurassic boundary only approximate*)
shale with eight beds of shelly limestone
H6 H5
H4 irregular limestone
H2 brown bituminous shale
H1 WHITE LIAS

Detailed section of the Blue Lias at Lyme Regis based on the work of Lang (1924), House (1985) and redrawn by West (2001).

The layers of Shales with Beef, above the Blue Lias, are also rhythmic but the limestones are mostly replaced by fibrous calcite or 'beef' so called because of a resemblance to the fibrous nature of a steak.

Above the unconformity, is the Gault Clay which is blue-black and very sticky. This unreliable material causes landslides when it is wet. Similar conditions occur at Folkestone Warren, Kent and Ventnor, Isle of Wight. In places there are rows of big concretions (large rounded boulders), known as cowstones, from the Upper Greensand.

The Jurassic rocks are often broken by faults produced by mid Jurassic tectonic movements, but the Upper Greensand and Chalk, above, lie undisturbed.

The appearance of the ammonite *Psiloceras* near the base of the Blue Lias marks the start of the Jurassic period.

Mercia Mudstone - Triassic

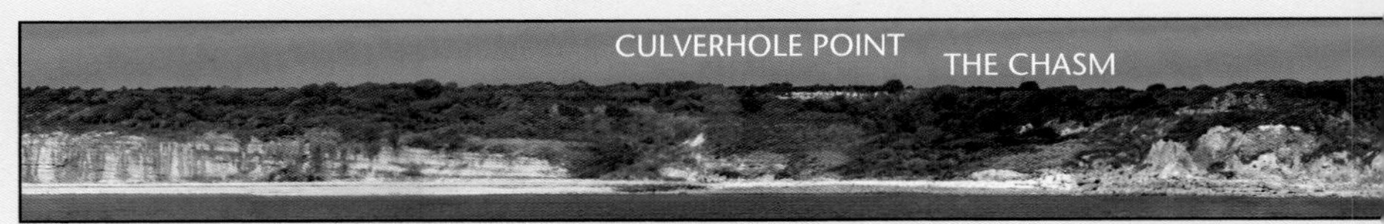

Penarth Beds

Slipped Upper Greensand forms sea cliff

Fault in Mercia Mudstone

Blue Lias

Blue Lias

Mercia Mudstone - Triassic

Slipped Chalk and Upper Greensand

Chalk slipped from cliff top to sea cliff

Fault White Lias

Blue Lias - Jurassic

The Cobb

Types of Landslide

Within the Reserve there are many types of landslides, rock falls, scree runs, mudslides, clay falls, block slides, rotational slides and gullies. Toppling failures occur in the Middle Chalk and Upper Greensand on the seaward edge of Goat Island. The 1969 slip at Charton Bay produced tonnes of liquified Upper Greensand mixed with Lias and there is intermittent activity throughout the Reserve.

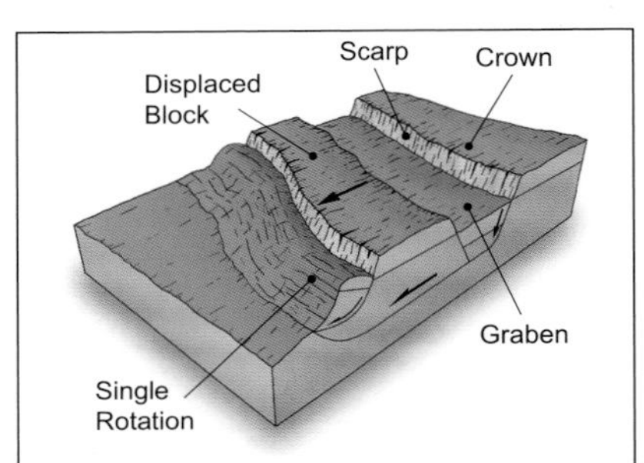

Block Slide

Block slides are often huge failures that slide on the bedding of the rocks. The cliff top subsides to form a 'graben' and chasm. Rotational slides are common at the toe.

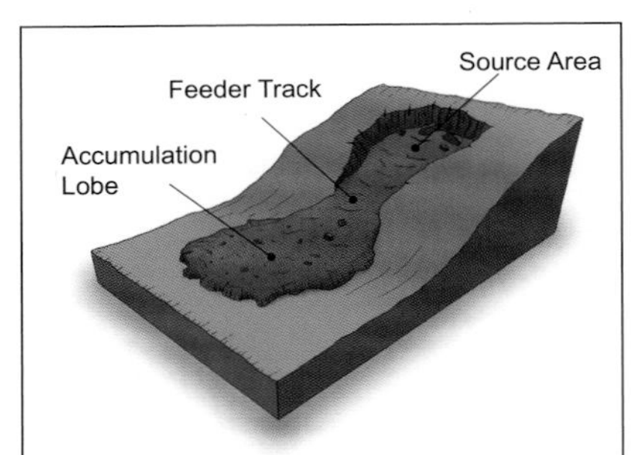

Mudslide

Mudslides are formed by the movement of clay, silt or sand, they can slide on their base and can also deform internally like porridge . When wet they flow like a liquid.

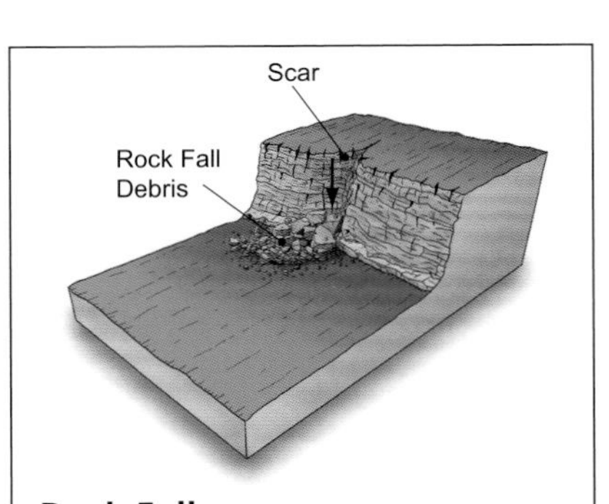

Rock Fall

Rock falls occur when material is detached from a steep cliff due to erosion, frost or joint opening. The material may 'run-out' from the base of the slope.

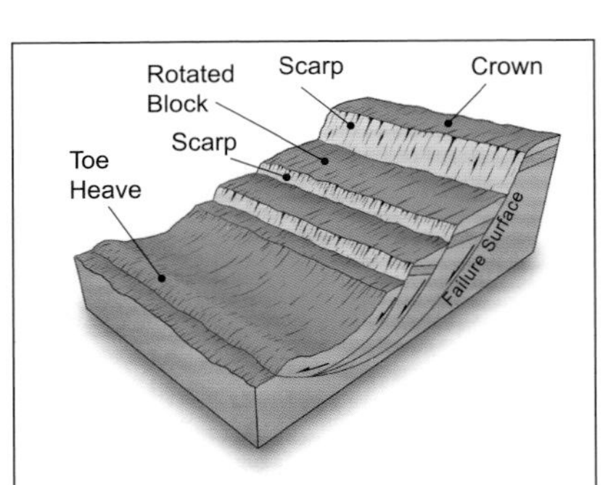

Multiple Rotational Slide

Blocks rotate because they move on a deep curved failure surface. They may be single or multiple.

April 2003

April 2004

May 2005

Monitoring Landslides

Investigating landslides is technically difficult. Analysis of aerial photography is often used but inadequate where there is abundant vegetation. Laser reflectors and satellite GPS systems have also been used. In the Undercliff a terrestrial photographic technique has been used by Exeter University to compare the same location over a period of time. For example, at the pumping station in February 1994 photographic evidence showed that after heavy rain there had been movement of 3.4m at the toe of the landslide in a week.

A GPS survey station used to measure movement.

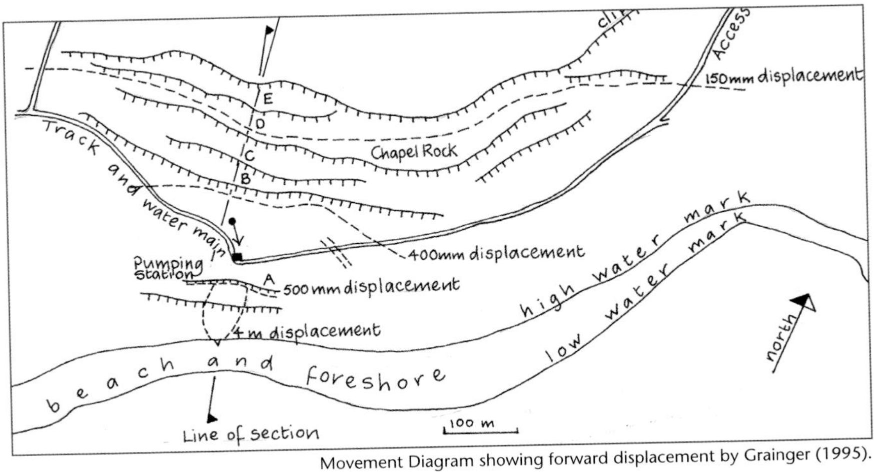

Movement Diagram showing forward displacement by Grainger (1995).

The Great Landslip of 1839

'The recent season of Christmas has been marked on the neighbouring line of coast by a convulsion so remarkable, from the extent, magnitude and picturesque change it has produced in the surface and general configuration of a line of country extending at least a mile in length, by half a mile in breadth ... that I cannot conceive that some account of it cannot fail to be acceptable. Although this convulsion can only be ascribed to the less dignified agency of the land springs constantly undermining the substrata; yet in grandeur of the disturbances it has occasioned, it far exceeds the ravages of earthquakes of Calabria and almost rivals of the vast volcanic fissures of the Val del Bore on the flanks of Aetna.'

L. E. Reed - View of the principal chasm showing the columnar masses (1840).

'Through the course of the following day (Christmas) a great subsidence took place through the fields ranging above Bendon Undercliff, forming a deep chasm or rather ravine, extending nearly three quarters of a mile in length, with a depth of 100 to 150 feet and a breadth exceeding 80 yards.'

Rev William D. Conybeare in the Edinburgh New Philosophic Journal.
Written in Axminster on 31st December 1839.

Conybeare was one of the leading geologists of the day and believed that the world had been created through a series of catastrophies. It was remarkable that he should be on the ground so quickly. The fact that another pioneer, William Buckland should be staying with him in Axminster, meant that this great landslip was one of the first to be studied by scientists who could provide a rational, if not complete, account of the cause.

'On the night of the 25th (December 1839) *one of the Coast Guard men, whilst on duty near the Undercliff, observed the sea to be in an extraordinary state of agitation. The beach on which he stood rose and fell. Amidst the breakers near the shore, something vast and dark appeared to be rising from the bottom of the sea amidst the noise of crashing rocks, flashing lights, attended with an intolerable stench. … In the morning, immediately in front of the Undercliff, which though still much rent and shaken, still retains its former position, there appeared a stupendous ridge of broken strata of blue lias, together with rocks of immense size immoveable by human power, covered with sea weed, shell fish and other marine productions. The elevation of this monstrous reef, extending more than a mile in length, and in some places two hundred yards in breadth, is not less than forty feet from the level of the sea.'*

An account in the Bath Journal of 20th January 1840.

G. Hawkins Junr. (Artist and Lithographer)
Culverhole Point near Lyme Regis. The Reef and Basin of Water (1840).

The Reef

Movements today are trivial compared with the events of 1839 and 1840 and there is nothing comparable with the chasm and the offshore reef which appeared then. Peter Orlando Hutchinson, who published 5 views of the Axmouth landscape in 1840, described:

> *'another feature which is no less remarkable; the rising of a reef of rocks from the bottom of the sea and the formation of a harbour or enclosed bay in consequence.'*

A rotational movement, in addition to old explanations, had been suggested in 1945 and later the Nature Conservancy's geologist, W.A. MacFadyen took up the issue of the upraised reef:

> *'The striking feature of the uprising … of offshore reefs or beaches … suggests that rotational shear slippage plays a controlling part in the mechanism of these movements, the reefs etc forming the uprising toe of the shear.'*

Today we know that this explanation applies only to the toe of the slip.

A view of the chasm and the Raised Reef of Rock and Marl.
J. Baker (artist) Printed (lithograph) by W. Gauci (c. 1840).

The Chasm

The great landslip at Bindon has been classified as a block slide. There is a subsiding area at the head of the slide called a graben. This is produced by the collapse of the strata as the main body of the landslide moves out from its source area. At Bindon the depression is called the Chasm and the body of the slide is Goat Island.

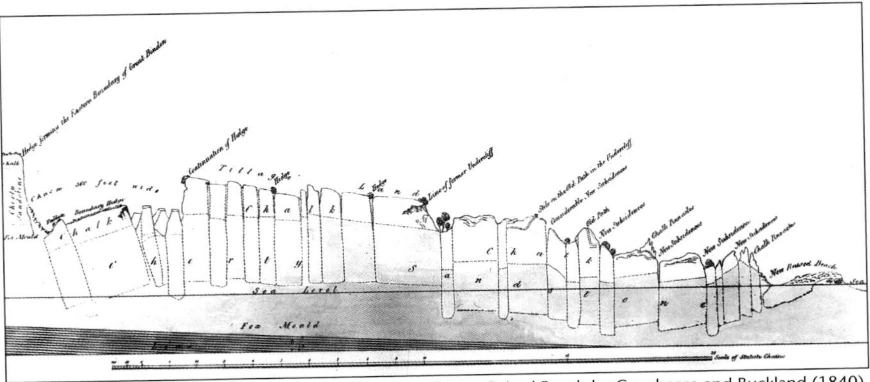

Geological section of the Chasm, Undercliff and New Raised Beach by Conybeare and Buckland (1840).

Peter Orlando Hutchinson - View of the landslip published in the Saturday Magazine Feb 8th 1840.

Movements at Whitlands

William Pitt the Younger described the Whitlands landslip of 1765, and accounts of other slips abound. The Axminster vicar and geologist Conybeare described a quarter mile long slip at Whitlands in Feb 1840. Other visitors, Woodward and Young mention the widening of the Great Cleft, a fissure along Pinhay Bay in 1906. Humble Pond lost its water as Lias Clay squeezed under the foreshore for 500 metres east of Humble Point between 28th February and 7th March 1961 and the beach was pushed up by some 4-5 metres.

Ken Gollop, one time fisherman and now Chairman of the Trustees of the Philpot Museum, describes how:

'We were potting along there when we found a wall of boulders which should have been down at sea level. It was very, very eerie and if we'd come in a fog we'd have wondered where the hell we were'.

The Great Cleft at Pinhay Cliff (from Rowe 1903).

On Stone by G. Hawkins Junr. - Uptilted house below Whitlands slip.

Recent movements below Chapel Rock

In 1935 Harts-tongue spring, emerging below the Chalk and Chert of Chapel Rock, was tapped by the South West Water Authority. A pumping station was built in front of the spring, to send water, via a holding reservoir, to Lyme Regis. Earth movements in 2001 finally made the pumping station unworkable as a result of 8 months of heavy rainfall. August and September 2000 had been unusually wet and, according to measurements at Pinhay, the period from October 2000 to March 2001 was the wettest 6 month period since records began there in 1868: over 33 inches of rain fell. Early in 2001 fissures began to appear along the coast path near the pumping station. Further west, towards Humble Point, movements of parallel ridges were destabilising the whole coastal cliff.

Chapel Rock (from Rowe 1903).

Peter Grainger, a geologist at Exeter University described in 1985 how seepage erosion from the sandy Foxmould could undermine the Chert Beds. These could then collapse with a rotational movement bringing the Chalk beds with them. They would be carried towards the sea on the disturbed sand. Eventually a block of the subsiding Chalk and Chert would come to rest on the Lias preventing further seepage erosion from the Foxmould.

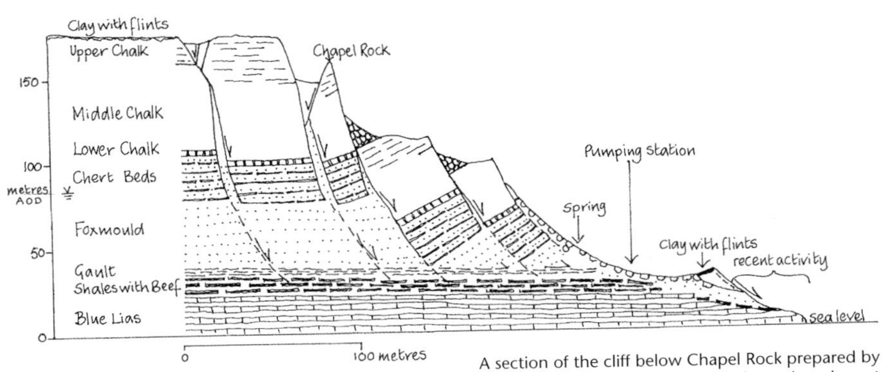

A section of the cliff below Chapel Rock prepared by Peter Grainger to show how slope failure takes place at the pumping station.

John Pitts and Geomorphology

'I hope that some active geologist who is capable of going up and down cliff faces and of hacking his way through the undergrowth of the landslip will come your way looking for a research programme'.

(Muriel Arber to Nature Conservancy Geologist W. A. MacFadyen 1956.)

It was some years before that 'active geologist' appeared in the form of John Pitts, a research student a Kings College London. Apart from the numerous papers he produced between 1974 and 1987, his Ph.D. thesis running to 710 pages provides an incredibly detailed mass of information on the geology, geomorphology and hydrogeology of the landslide area.

As well as working on the ground Pitts used the wonderful contemporary prints and later photographs to try to reconstruct the mechanisms of failure. He also published a definitive history in the Proceedings of the Dorset Natural History and Archaeological Society. Illustrated above is Mary Buckland's drawing of Goat Island and the Chasm 30 December 1839.

Starting at the back scar or inland cliff and moving towards the toe, each facet was picked up and traced laterally, using tapes and pacing. It was followed and measured until its conclusion. Then he would proceed along his predetermined line to the toe. With compass and hand held inclinometer, very accurate slope angles could be quickly found. With aerial photographs and earlier Ordnance Survey maps Pitts could eventually analyse major units like Haven Cliff or a profile to Humble Point. In all he listed 47 slope failure areas or units and in a table suggested the likely mechanism of failure, and the characteristics of the unit that could lead to failure or slippage.

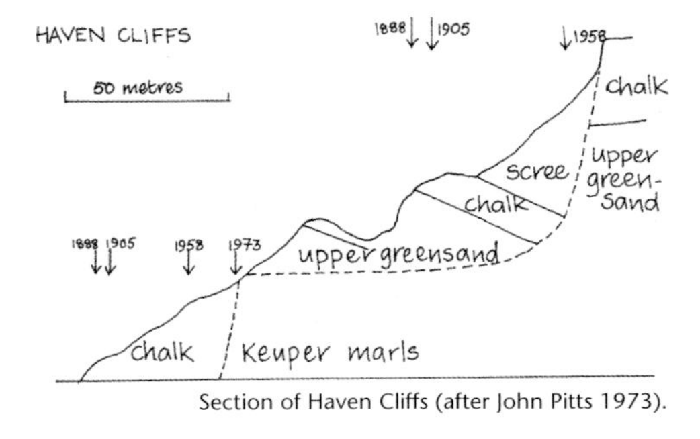

Section of Haven Cliffs (after John Pitts 1973).

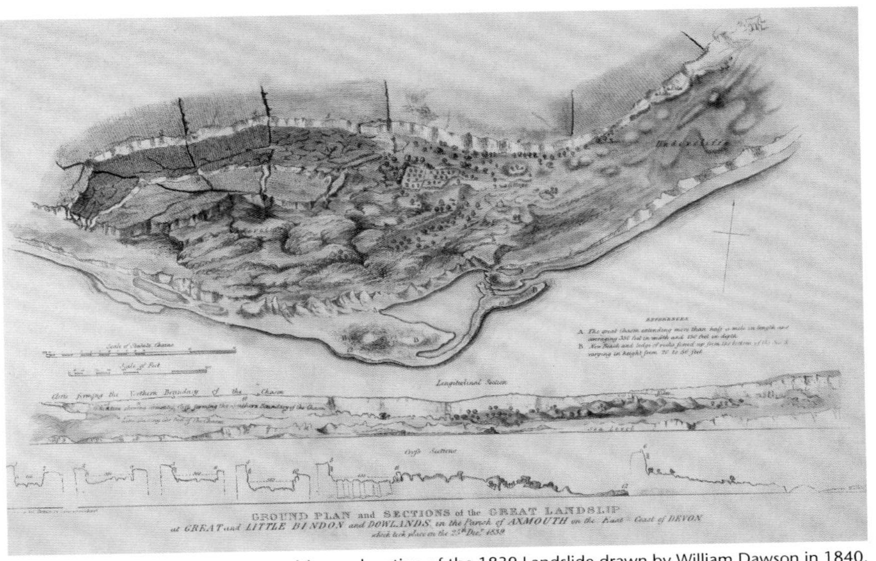

Map and section of the 1839 Landslide drawn by William Dawson in 1840.

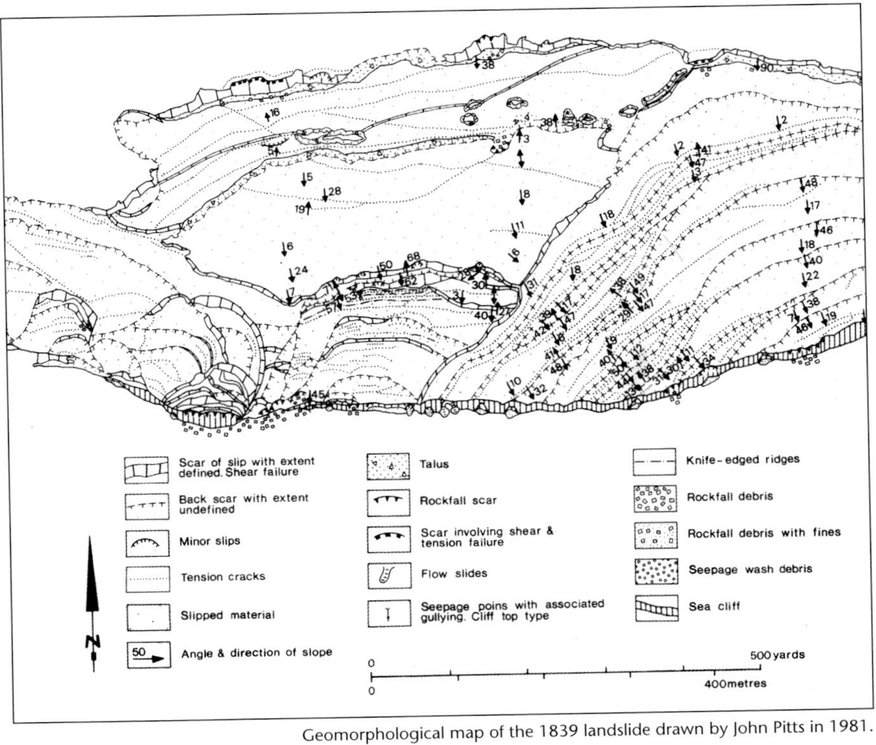

Geomorphological map of the 1839 landslide drawn by John Pitts in 1981.

Pioneers of a New Science

The properties at Whitlands and Pinney (now Pinhay) were owned by the Oke family in 1765. In 1684 Walter Oke of Axmouth married Dinah Broughton of Combpyne. Their three surviving sons lived in Combpyne, Whitlands and Pinney.

In 1783 another marriage linked the Oke family to the Bucklands, a union that was to influence the history of science. Elizabeth Oke and the Rev Charles Buckland, curate at Colyton with Shute, were to have 6 children of whom the oldest, William, became the first professor of geology at Oxford University and later Dean of Westminster.

The 1839 Landslip became so famous that a piece of music, The Landslip Quadrille was written to celebrate the event.

By chance William and his wife Mary were staying in Axminster with the Rev W. D. Conybeare at the time of the Great Landslip. Mary's drawings, (page 26) made soon after the event, still provide evidence about the nature of the slip. Together with nine other plates they provide an inspiring record of the event. W. Dawson, civil engineer and surveyor, prepared the plates from drawings, the Rev. Conybeare provided a geological memoir and Professor Buckland reviewed the whole volume.

'representing the changes produced on the coast of East Devon between Axmouth and Lyme Regis by the subsidence of the land and elevation of the bottom of the sea',

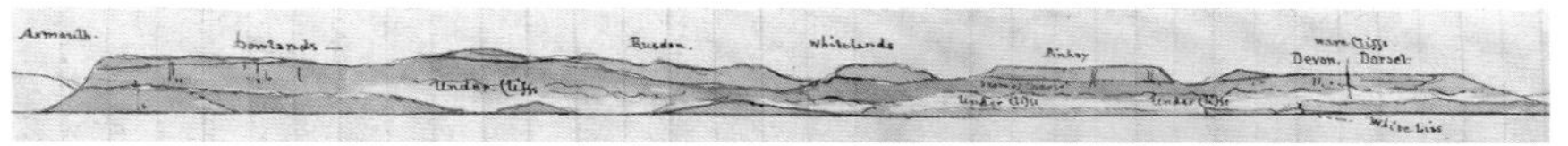

Drawing by Henry De la Beche showing the Undercliffs in 1818-19.

Another pioneer was Henry De La Beche who founded the Geological Survey and the Royal School of Mines. His section (above) is probably the first detailed depiction of the stratigraphy of the cliffs of the Jurassic Coast.

Drawing by William Buckland in 1823 of the East Devon coast from the book Reliquiae Diluvianae (Relics of the Flood).

Fossilists at Lyme

'We were not by any means, prepared for so scientific and luminous a statement of geological facts and illustrations as the Rev Gentleman contrived to make his medium of transmitting to us. Some fine specimens of organic remains were exhibited. The anatomical structure of these the Rev Mr C. most perspicuously described'.

This early reference to scientific geology comes from Felix Farley's review of a talk on 28th April 1825 given by Conybeare to the Bristol Philosophical and Literary Society.

Conybeare was especially interested in reptiles and when Mary Anning found the first almost complete skeleton of a *Plesiosaurus* he wrote to De la Beche about a visit from Buckland who had brought news of the sale of the *Plesiosaurus* to the Duke of Buckingham for £200. Buckland's visit had diverted Conybeare who wondered *'whether a parson has ever before, or since, been lured from his sermon by a Plesiosaurus'.*

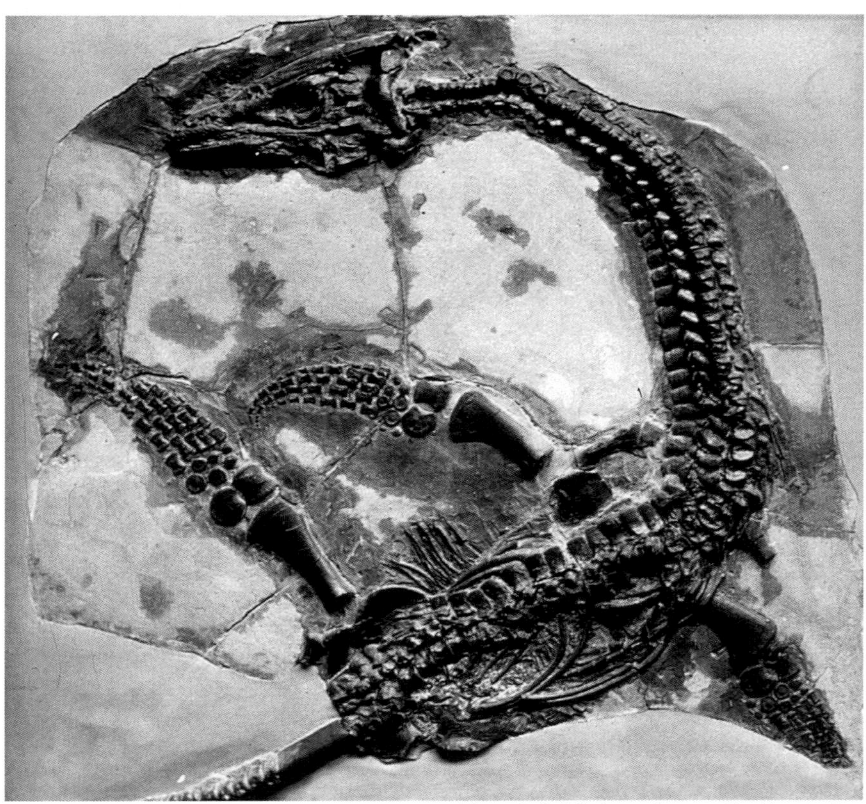

A large-skulled *Plesiosaur* discovered by Mary Anning.

A sketch of Mary Anning by De la Beche.

Rev. William Conybeare.

Sir Henry De la Beche.

Dr. William Buckland.

Mary Anning is the best known fossil collector from Lyme, but Elizabeth Philpot, one of four sisters, was also accumulating a collection and in 1829 Buckland wrote about suspecting the existence of 'the Pterodactyle' in the Lias at Lyme having found

'in the cabinet of Miss Philpot a thin elongated fragment of flat bone which appears to be the jaw of a Pterodactyle; it is set with very minute, flat, lancet shaped teeth.'

Later when the Geologists' Association first visited Lyme in 1889 their Director, Horace B. Woodward, read notes about the early fossilists including 'Captain Cury' who had collected curiosities from Charmouth in the 1790s and Thomas Hawkins who blew up whole cliffs in his search for ichthyosaurs.

Cast of *Ichthyosaurus conybeari* from the Philpot Museum.

Some of the Fossils

Mussels and other two shelled (bivalve) molluscs are as common today as their relatives were in the Jurassic seas. Scallops and Oysters can easily be recognised as they have changed so little over the ages. Oyster fossils like *Gryphaea arcuata*, sometimes known as the Devil's Toenail are often eroded onto the beach. Fossil nautiloids, which like ammonites, are related to squids and cuttlefish, are also found.

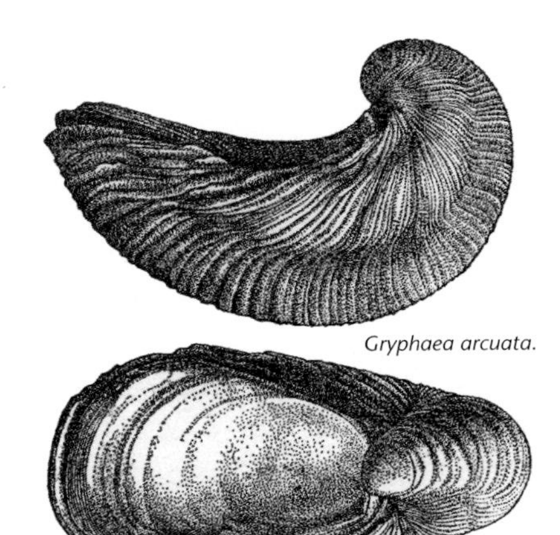

Gryphaea arcuata.

No ammonites lived in the shallow British seas of the late Triassic but as waters deepened, bringing connections with distant seas, they swarmed in. Unlike the bivalves they underwent rapid evolutionary change so that individual species are associated with particular layers of sedimentary rock and therefore used to split up geological time. Large ammonites can be seen on Monmouth Beach. Please leave them for others to enjoy.

Arnioceras semicostatum.

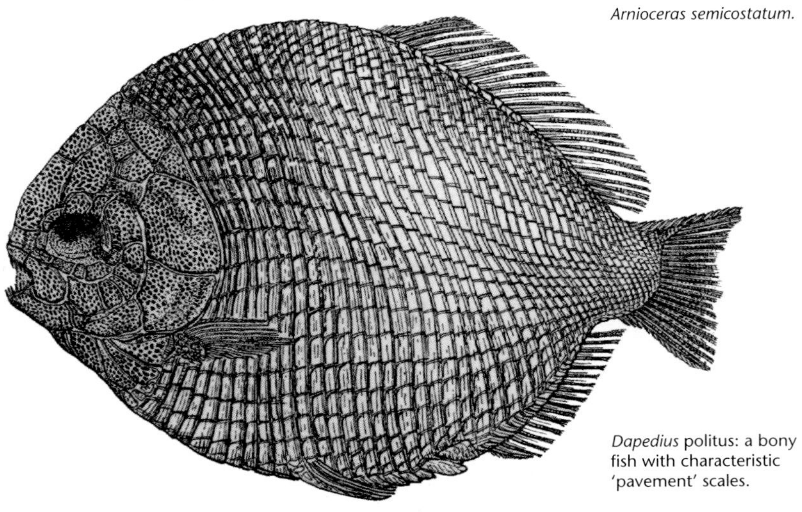

Dapedius politus: a bony fish with characteristic 'pavement' scales.

Several fossil locations in the Undercliff are of Special Scientific Interest. Entire skeletons, including those of ichthyosaurs and plesiosaurs, have been extracted from the Blue Lias and Shales with Beef. The Saurian Shales, near the top of the Blue Lias, is characterised by Mesozoic fish with 7 species of sharks and rays, 31 species of bony fish and a 70cm Coelacanth (a rare fish from the Blue Lias).

The cowstones of the Upper Greensand often yield fossil tube worms. Numerous echinoids (fossil sea urchins), the object of Charles' search in 'The French Lieutenants Woman' are also found in Cretaceous rocks together with Bivalves and ammonites.

The giant ammonite Arietites.

Picturesque Paintings

Pinhay became a popular destination for Georgian and Regency visitors attracted to Lyme Regis by the new fashion for sea bathing and the romantic discovery of wild nature and landscape.

In 1773 William Pitt, the Earl of Chatham, wrote, after a visit to Lyme, of

'breathing the purest air imaginable, pursuing health through paths of amusement over these hills which abound with striking beauties of nature.'

Two early pictures of the 'romantic' Undercliff date from 1784 when Copplestone Warre Bampfyld, from Hestercombe in Somerset, painted Whitlands Cliff and the Umble Rock. The latter is now so obscured by trees and by Ivy that few know of its existence.

Whitlands Cliff

The Umble Rock

Cliff Top Estates

The freedom to use the Undercliff paths, valued by fishermen, stonemasons and the preventive men, whose job was to control smuggling, was lost in 1834 when John Ames, having bought the Pinhay Estate, built a wall to mark its boundary and sealed off the path. Later, after trials and appeals, the path was reopened but with high walls on either side of the narrow way and with a high narrow stile at the entrance.

FAR FAMED PINNEY CLIFFS
This highly picturesque and unique
FREEHOLD PROPERTY

The eulogy bestowed on these grounds rich in the treasures of an Antidiluvian World by the illustrious Earl Chatham is too valuable and apposite not to be now recorded. I have heard, I have read of Pinney but after all the highest reach of my fancy never pictured a spot so diversified or its beauties so fitted for consultation or peculiar in its combinations.

... This place must be visited again to make the worth of Lyme understood, a place upon which, as it has been well observed, the Fossilist and Geologist look as the Sportsman does on Melton Mowbray.

It may well be said that here a struggle seems to take place between the Genius of the mountain and that of the Vale. Here is met with Fertility – there the rugged Cliff. There the majestically towering

WHITE CHAPEL ROCK

bidding proud defiance: here gently swelling hills studded with Trees of luxuriant growth a happy combination of

ALPINE SCENERY and ITALIAN LANDSCAPE

Parts of the sale details of Pinney Mansion and Estate in 1834.

Lithograph of Rousdon from 'The Building News' 26th June 1874.

The Rousdon Estate (formerly Allhallows School) above Rousdon Cliffs.

Ames had bought Pinhay for 8000 guineas and completed a new house in 1847. It was twenty years later that Henry William Peek, rich from the family tea business, started work on a new mansion further to the west. His estate, covering all the tiny parish of Rousdon and parts of Axmouth, extended, like the Pinhay Estate, into the Undercliff. A mansion like Peek's, in such an isolated site, needed to be as self sufficient as possible, so the water supply was taken from a spring half way down the cliff where a steam pumping station was installed. He also created a quarry near the top of the Reserve, planted rhododendron and other exotics and made a track down to Humble Point so that specially imported donkeys could bring marble from a convenient wreck to create his staircase and tessellated floors. This track finally collapsed in a mudslide in 1969.

In 1937 the Peeks sold the estate and most of the Rousdon part became Allhallows School.

Cottages in The Undercliff

The Pinhay Estate was bounded by East and West Cliff Cottages, also known as Stones' and Stanley's after the occupiers.

Further west was Rock Cottage where William Critchard and his family lived until the Great Landslip destroyed it. Several years later the stone from this cottage was reused to build Landslip Cottage a little further east. Here, from about 1901, Richard and Mary Gapper lived, eventually with 10 children. Elizabeth, the youngest, was born in the cottage in 1903 and Annie, their second child, is often associated with teas in the Undercliff.

Tea at Landslip Cottage: Muriel Arber, a famous amateur geologist recalled a visit in 1928 with tea and cakes and surrounded by Chaffinches.

Annie, who loved the cottage and the Undercliff, was there until 1950 and Norman Barns, a Voluntary Warden, knew her. He recalls hearing about her father Richard who did coppicing work and cut Ivy for cattle fodder; a job he didn't like as adders fell out as the Ivy was stripped from the trees. He also made pea sticks, bean poles and wattle hurdles and there were still a few pigs and sheep to look after.

In 1976 another Voluntary Warden, Tom Wallace, visited Mary's daughter Elizabeth, then living in Axminster. She had married Arthur, a descendant of the William Critchard who had lived in Rock Cottage. Elizabeth described how white stones had been placed along the path down the cliff from Dowlands to make walking at night and on foggy days safer and recalled how their water came from a well a little to the west of the house, near a Box hedge which her father trimmed into a cottage loaf shape. One of Elizabeth's sons, Roger, can remember spending Christmas in Landslip Cottage when he was four, with the family gathered around the open fire in the kitchen.

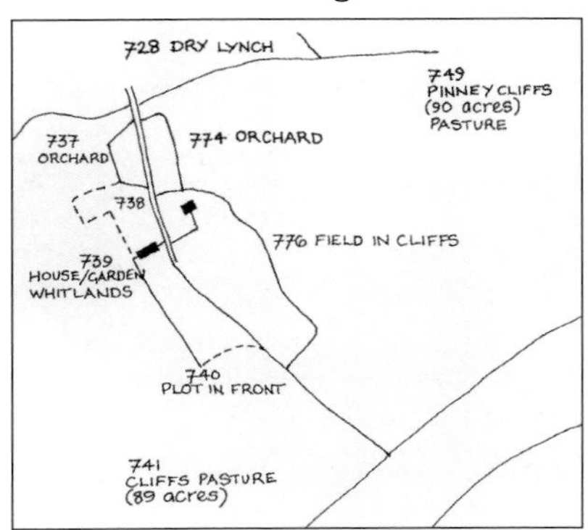

Tithe map of 1840 showing what is now known as West Cliff Cottage. Note the extent of pasture in the surrounding cliffs.

Members of the Gapper family outside Cliff Cottage.

Towards a National Nature Reserve

The Undercliffs were not on the 1942 list of 55 proposed National Nature Reserves nor the 1947 list of 73 sites prepared by Julian Huxley. A visit by Sir Arthur Tansley, founder Chairman of the Nature Conservancy, on 16th October 1949, began moves towards National Nature Reserve status.

Tansley wrote

> *'It is ... of importance to all geologists that this feature (the Chasm) should be preserved undisturbed'*

and that

> *'natural ashwoods ... examples of self sown virgin woodland, an extremely rare phenomenon in present day Britain, are naturally of high interest and their preservation of great ecological importance'.*

By 1950 the site had been proposed as a National Nature Reserve and a visit by Norman Moore (South West Regional Officer for the Nature Conservancy) in 1953 attempted to find out more about the potential Reserve. He was impressed by the wealth of micro-habitats and thought that it would be worthwhile to study small semi-isolated communities on chalk grassland and on the bare earth resulting from landslides. Norman Moore has played a leading part in virtually every episode in the history of organised nature conservation in Britain.

Norman Moore examining a rare damselfly in 1953.

Most of the area was designated as a National Nature Reserve on 16th March 1955 with Rousdon and Charton Cliffs being added on 17th July 1956.

Fifty years later we can celebrate successful conservation measures which acknowledge the contributions of these pioneers. Immense challenges remain but more active management in removing invasive non-native species is now in place.

Solitary Cuckoo Wasp (*Nysson trimaculatus*) A survey of ants, bees and wasps, was among projects suggested by Norman Moore.

TOWARDS A NATIONAL NATURE RESERVE

'I know few pleasures greater than standing in a newly established nature reserve which one has helped to set up. You feel that you have made a special link with the plants and animals around you and with the people who will come to look at their descendants in the future.'

Norman Moore From 'The Bird of Time', 1987. Cambridge University Press.

The Nature Conservancy and Tom Wallace

Tom Wallace identifying a fungus.

Hamish Archibald, Assistant Regional Officer for the Nature Conservancy in the South West, wrote the first Management Plan for the Undercliffs in 1965. With his forester's interests his plan emphasised the role of the woody plants in the Reserve explaining that although there were 33 large tree and shrub species that were native, there were also 30 exotics, perhaps as a consequence of the mild climate and Ames' arboretum. Although competition between the native and introduced species was seen as interesting, the exotics were to become a threat as rhododendron, Cherry Laurel and, worst of all, Holm Oak have continued to spread into open grassland and soft cliffs. Rotational scrub clearance on Goat Island was part of the plan, as was maintenance of some existing glades and the opening up of other sites, notably some of the ponds.

Tom Wallace, who later joined the staff at Allhallows School, was getting to know the Undercliff and rediscovered *Gentianella anglica* (a small and rare gentian) on Dowlands cliff edge. In June 1954 he led a special excursion of 65 members of the Devonshire Association who were very impressed with the plant life. He ensured that a great deal more was known about the Reserve. In 1963 Tom Wallace produced a booklet, enlarged and updated in 1966 and 1976. In all, his species lists ran to 90 sheets and mentioned 1600 different species in 21 groups.

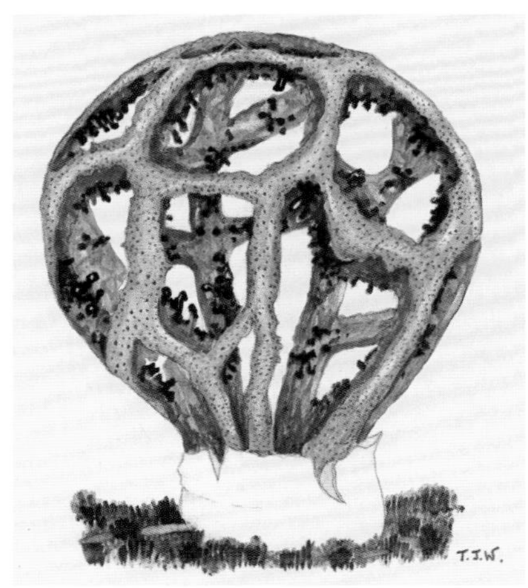

A notable discovery in June 1958 was the rare, extraordinary and malodorous *Clathrus ruber*, painted by Tom Wallace.

'From 1957 to 1969, while on the staff of the School, I myself devoted countless hours to the task of recording; I was also able to encourage many of my students to help me effectively. Over the years I found myself leading a large number of visiting parties, from natural history societies, schools, universities etc each of which usually included a specialist or two in some biological subject.'

(Tom Wallace, Recollections)

Dark Bush-cricket. Described by Tom Wallace as a brisk chirper by day and night.

Tom Wallace recalled 'a wigging far worse than any sergeant major' when a bee orchid was picked on a botanical expedition to Goat Island.

Norman Barns, voluntary warden

In 1977, soon after John Pitts begun his studies, Norman Barns became a Voluntary Warden. Over the next 25 years he would spend even more time in the Undercliff than John. Norman first walked the coast path in 1927 and often maintained that others lacked a time perspective; he had seen the spread of Holm Oak and scrub.

Norman worked closely with Elaine Franks whose Undercliff sketchbook was published in 1989. Perhaps it was her short sightedness that made her particularly fond of invertebrates which, though often neglected form a vital part of soft cliff communities. A bee enthusiast from Yorkshire identified 33 species of wasps and bees and pronounced the 16th July 1985 as his best day ever.

Norman was involved with a new Management Plan for the Reserve in 1992 which considered the process of succession in the form of diagrams.

Conservation of the Peregrine Falcon was one of the concerns in the second Management Plan.

Bombus lucorum from Elaine Franks' sketchbook 'The Undercliff'.

Norman Barns found 24 sites of Dormouse activity in the Reserve.

Thus the Reserve is shaped by landsliding and by management. That the former often determines events can be appreciated by a note from invertebrate expert Alan Stubbs, who had discovered a cranefly new to Britain in a cascade down Haven Cliff in 1989 but found, in 1997, that the best stream habitat there had been destroyed by landslides.

Norman, who described himself as *'older than most of the trees'* regarded his role as *'preventing camping, recording plant and animal life, coppicing and creating viewpoints along the path.'*

Surveys and Management

Over the years a variety of surveys have been carried out by professionals and enthusiastic amateurs including Voluntary Wardens. An early study found over 150 species of fungi and, in 1972, 89 lichens were found in a day's surveying. In 1980-81, 254 fresh water invertebrates were found.

Five days in July 1995 recorded another 150 invertebrates concentrating on Diptera (flies) and Hymenoptera (ants, bees and wasps) but this was surpassed in 2003 when 292 species, including 64 nationally scarce or Red Data Book invertebrates, were recorded. These data books are lists of threatened species with details of their status and ecology.

Digital mapping of vegetation confirms that the limited intervention policy provides a rich mosaic of habitats. The mapping and vegetation surveys of complex areas by South West Ecological Surveys (2002 – 2003) also provide a baseline for future comparisons.

Greater Butterfly Orchid; concentration of this rare plant increases after scrub clearance.

The current Management Plan (2003) continues to allow the natural development of plant communities and to safeguard features of special interest. Coastal processes will be allowed to operate unimpeded, local people will be involved and quality interpretation provided in the form of guided walks and managed public access via the coast path and beach. The existing sense of wilderness will be maintained and access away from the coast path is restricted. All must be grateful to East Devon's Countryside Service for keeping this path in good condition.

Some invasive species are controlled and ponds, glades and grassland are managed. This has led to an increase in the diversity and extent of grassland communities on Goat Island and the Plateau which in turn has improved conditions for many invertebrates.

Stratiomys potamida: a nationally scarce Soldier Fly (see page 48).

Bullfinches were found at unusually high densities in a Common Bird Census (1994-98).

Soft Cliffs

The area of soft cliff below Pinhay is extraordinary as islands of vegetation and dead trees 'float' among patches of bare wet earth and shallow temporary pools. These special conditions help to create the diverse vegetation types that have led to the designation of the soft cliffs between Sidmouth and West Bay as a Special Area of Conservation (SAC) under the European Habitats Directive.

Burnet Moths are common on the cliffs.

Wherever sandy strata have a sunny aspect, warmth loving bees and wasps make their burrows. Pinhay Warren is one of the flatter of these soft cliffs, parts of unstable areas at Culverhole and Charton Bay are on steeper slopes, while much of Haven Cliff is nearly vertical.

Soil movements kill the trees which eventually slide over the cliff.

The invertebrate fauna continue to provide exciting discoveries and the soft rock cliffs are among the most important invertebrate habitats in the country. There is a Spider-hunter Wasp with Red Data Book status, a Digger Wasp, a Mining Bee restricted to the coast of East Devon and Dorset, and Cuckoo Bees. Short palped Craneflies, a Fungus Gnat and scarce Soldier and Hopper Parisitoid Flies are all present.

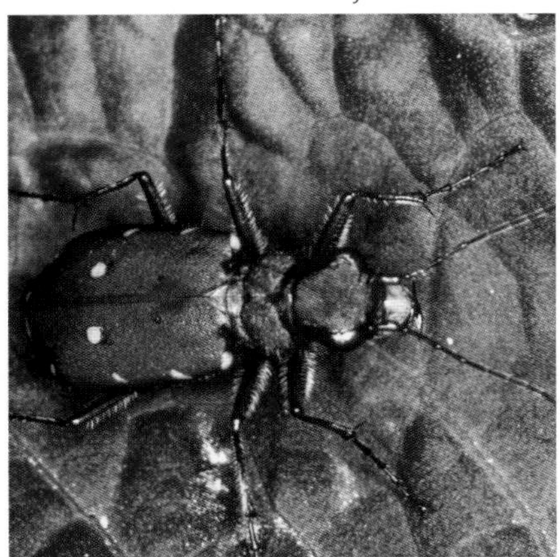

Tiger Beetles enjoy areas of bare soil.

Pinhay Warren - unstable 'soft' cliff above the Blue Lias.

Solitary Bees are characteristic of sandy cliffs.

A mating pair of Dingy Skippers.

Chalk Grassland

Chalk grasslands are not very extensive but occur on Goat Island at Bindon and the Plateau towards Dowlands. Phil Page, Site Manager since 1994, recollects that both these areas were overgrown when he spent his first day cutting and raking in 1987. He was keen that the grassland habitats should be improved and initiated three-day work sessions, twice a year, to achieve this. These two areas of calcareous (chalk) grassland, and other small glades and soft cliffs, have some of the most valued plants and insects in the Reserve.

The unusual management makes for unusual vegetation. Many grasses typical of grazed grassland are not found, while the presence of many woody seedlings cause botanists to classify it more as calcareous scrub although to most of us it looks like grassland. The commonest plants are Glaucous Sedge, Eyebright, Salad Burnet and Birds-foot Trefoil.

These grasslands have distinctive species. Harebell and Rock Rose with its associated butterfly, the Brown Argus, are limited to the Plateau. Goat Island sometimes has over a hundred Autumn Ladies Tresses and up to 30,000 Autumn Gentians and the Plateau is the stronghold of the tiny, annual Early Gentian. This is a Biodiversity Action Plan species (which indicates a Government conservation priority) and the site is therefore of national importance.

Yellow Meadow Ants make conspicuous nests on the grassland.

More than 100 Marbled Whites fly over Goat Island grassland.

Rose-spotted plant bug, a common species on dry grassland.

Pyramidal Orchid: One of eight orchid species found in the Undercliffs.

Succession in the Chasm

Succession is the replacement of one plant community by another over a period of time. In the Undercliffs this process starts as the bare soil created by landslides is colonised by plants with wind blown seeds. In the Chasm this has taken place uninterrupted ever since 1839.

There was not, as is often quoted, virgin soil after the landslip, for the fields that subsided had been arable. Initially however, the disturbance left things bare as the many early prints show. Accounts describing *'the wonderful labyrinth of ruins'* when the King of Saxony visited in 1844 and how *'it too much resembles a gravel pit'* (Murray's Guide 1859) confirm the early barren nature of the Chasm.

By 1900 Baring Gould refers to *'brambles growing in the wildest abundance, clawed like the paws of a panther.'*

One hundred years later the Chasm is largely filled with mature Ash trees but there are a few Field Maples and enormous Hazels. The abundant nettles are fed by fertiliser running off the fields above. They contrast with the few herb-rich north facing slopes which, as a result of careful management, remain on screes below Goat Island.

The Chasm, Goat Island and Culverhole.

The Chasm in 1870 showing the beginning of plant colonisation.

The Chasm in 1947 showing well established woodland.

The Chasm in 2003 now covered with dense scrub and woodland.

The Coast Path

The coast path is the only way to access the Reserve. It is described here in convenient sections from east to west. It is dangerous to leave this path as deep fissures and unstable ground are constant hazards.

From Devonshire Head to Whitlands

Walter White, on his walk from London to Lands End in 1850, found the east end of the Undercliff *'all so broken up with steep banks, hummocks and knolls as to form a very chaos'*. In the same year Roland Brown's Guide described it in similar terms *'a chaotic mass of hills, steep banks and knolls'*. What White described as *'fertile pasturage'* where *'flocks of sheep quietly browsed'* has now become sycamore woodland. The walls built in 1834 by John Ames, the owner of the Pinhay Estate, now lined *'a dull, ill natured, envious looking path'*.

Today walkers on the path need the steps which go up and down among slips which occurred between 1961 and 1964. In 2003 some of the path was rerouted to drier ground and in the same year English Nature, with volunteer help, cleared in and around Ravine Pond which is spring filled and only formed in 1961. Through a gap in Ames wall one could once reach a popular grassy picnic spot. Close to the sea landslides carry dead trees across the soft bare cliffs.

Coast path west of Pinhay.

Soft cliffs above Pinhay Bay.

Most Silver-washed Fritillaries are found around Whitlands.

In a wet area are the remains of pipes and a hydraulic ram which pumped water to Pinhay House above and along another recent path diversion are a number of Small-leaved Lime trees. Near the track to Pinhay is a huge Lime with V shaped double trunks and a Beech which featured in the film of 'The French Lieutenants Woman'.

The coast path continues as a surfaced track to the pumping station through a well wooded area with Pines, large Beech trees and many invasive, non native, Holm Oak and Cherry Laurel. Above is Chapel Rock where non-conformists worshipped in the 1660s.

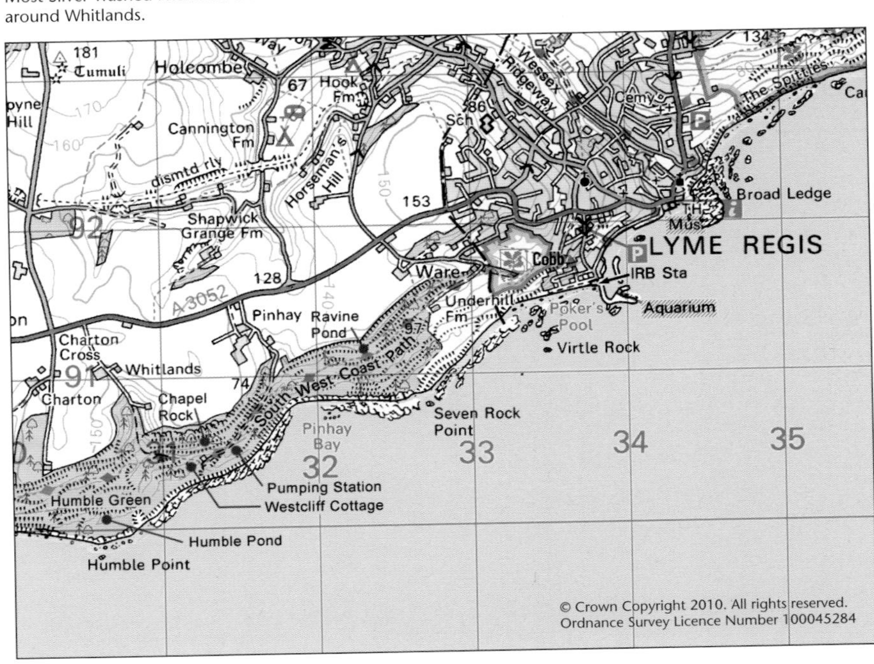

From Whitlands to Dowlands Cliffs

Walter White met difficulties at Whitlands where *'one of those amphitheatre like hollows so frequent along the coast, with space enough for a cottage, an orchard and a little field'* encouraged him to pause.

A man who was digging told him he could go no further, no one could get through the tangle nor go round it. Today the District Council's Countryside Rangers make sure that the coast path is clear by removing fallen trees and cutting back brambles.

The route of this section of the path lies between landslide pressure ridges and in early spring Golden Saxifrage and Primroses are followed by Wild Garlic, Bugle and Sanicle. The path climbs, over tree roots and flights of steps until, passing an old Yew, a view of the inland cliff appears. Charton, is the highest coastal point in Devon and the steep sandstone cliffs make a popular Peregrine perch.

There could be as many as 40 pairs of Marsh Tit in the Reserve.

Field maple on Whitlands Cliff.

Raven.

A long series of steps takes the path down to the chimney of the Rousdon Mansion pumping station. Despite an obvious private access route to the beach visitors are reminded that they must stick to the coast path which soon passes the ruins of the old engineer's cottage which subsided in 1911.

In 2004/5 rhododendrons were removed from around the ruin, opening up a view to the sea. The path steps take one upwards until there are good views of the chalk cliffs, where a Raven's nest, a big pile of sticks, can often be seen. At some stage in the distant past the great block of chalk that forms the Plateau slid down from here.

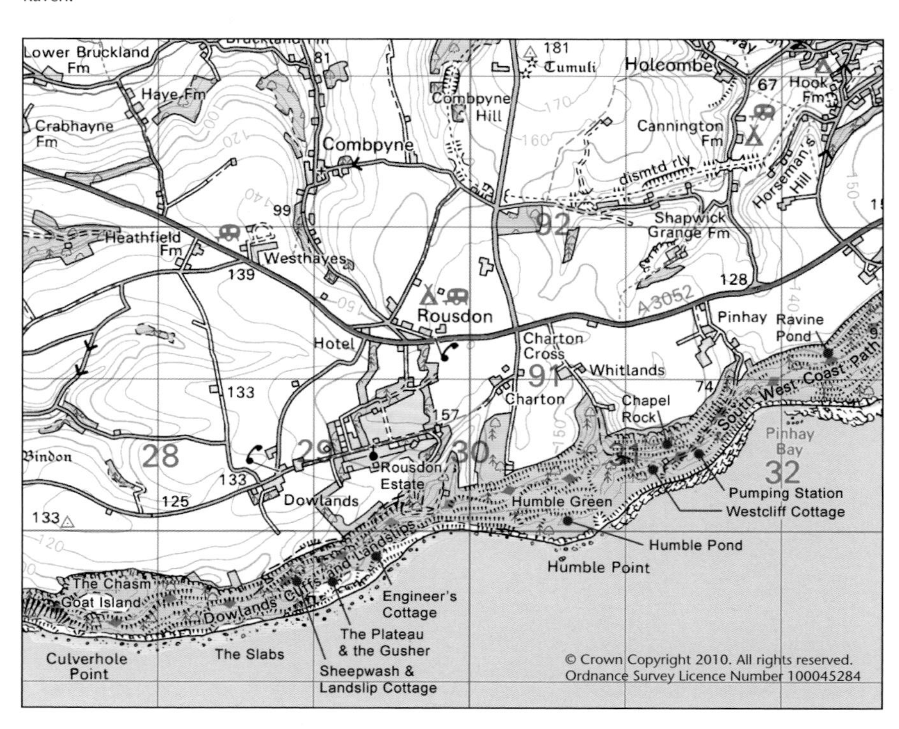

Dowlands Cliffs to Bindon Cliffs

Clearance of this section of the path in 2004 has revealed the walls of Landslip Cottage, burned down in 1953, and the old sheep wash dating from 1800, which is a reminder that all the land west from Rousdon was pasture until about 1900. Some Hazel was coppiced and one glade, recently recoppiced, has been colonised by Wood Spurge and St John's Wort. Wild Daffodils flourish on the inland cliff side of the path.

THE WORLD FAMOUS
DOWLANDS CLIFF AND LANDSLIP

Embracing the MOST BEAUTIFUL AND UNIQUE
CLIFF SCENERY IN ENGLAND
In all about
164 Acres
Offering tremendous possibilities

Nor is this scenery to photograph and forget but a part of Devon
STEEPED IN TRADITION AND ROMANCE
The whole forms
A veritable Paradise for Lovers of Nature

Extracted from the catalogue for the sale of the Peek Estate on 14th September 1937.

Bugle is a distinctive plant along the coast path.

Large rocks from a 1790 landslip are found just west of the site of Rock Cottage and there was another building on the left of the unexpectedly straight Avenue. Throughout the woodland, and where it emerges into an area of calcareous scrub, look out for the parasitic Ivy Broom-rape. This area of scrub is one of the few places away from the soft cliffs where the local Wood White butterfly, with its distinctive slow flapping oval wings, can be seen. Goat Island is above, separated from the path by a series of steep, narrow ridges on which Roe Deer often graze.

Undercliffs are one habitat for the declining Wood White.

Narrow-leaved Everlasting Sweet Pea and Madder climb over the scrub in unstable Culverhole below the coast path. Here sandy Gault forms the back scar of a landslide. Recently created steps, down and then up, follow the edge of this slip. Culverhole has productive and diverse wet flushes dominated by Black Bog Rush, Fragrant Orchid and Marsh Helleborine.

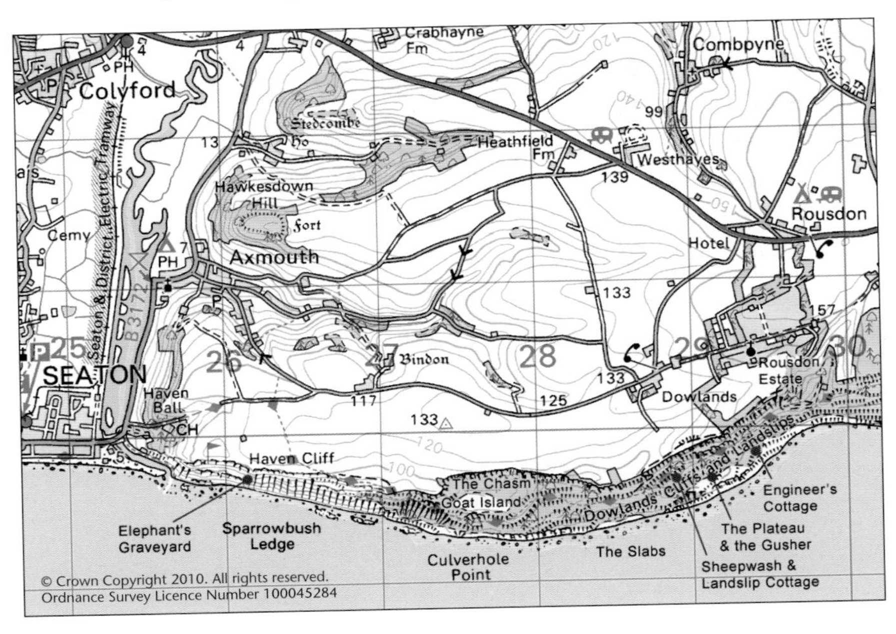

Lyme Regis to below the Plateau

Although the views are best from a boat a walk along the coast is possible if tides permit. On Monmouth Beach the winter tide line is often littered with fallen trees and the roots of horsetails and reeds from the slopes of Ware. When the steep cliffs replace these gentler slopes, mounds of detritus pile up on the beach, the layers of Blue Lias are obscured by a mixture of rock types from above. It is hard to imagine the quarrymen, railway, brick works and industrial activity of the past.

Oyster Catchers often provide noisy company.

On the beach a mix of stones can be found including silicaceous brown Chert and knobbly, often white, Flint and Chalk that has been brought from further west by long shore drift. 'Beef', grey slightly dappled rock has come from the cliffs above. Along this exposed shore brown sea weeds show their typical zonation, with upper shore species more tolerant of exposure than those in zones nearer the low tide line. The tube worm *Sabellaria* forms honey comb like mounds and soft limestone is riddled with bore holes due to the bivalved Piddock or the boring shell, *Hiatella*.

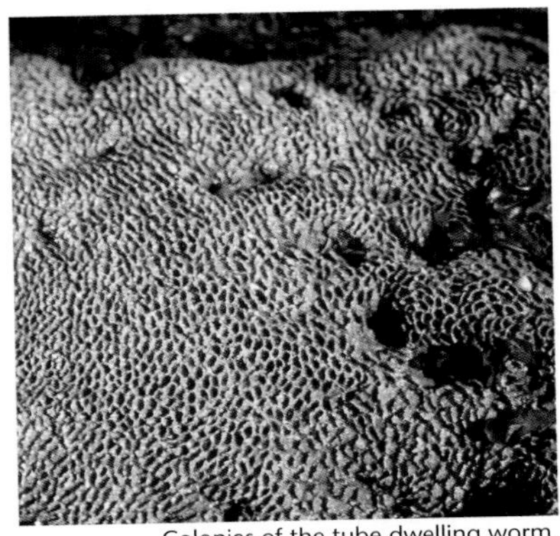

Colonies of the tube dwelling worm, Sabellaria, cover many Blue Lias slabs.

Beyond the Blue Lias of Pinhay the White Lias is collapsing and all the way to Humble Point the upper beach is a chaos of fallen trees, fresh and smoothed limestone cobbles and, below the pumping station, pipes and waterfalls. Beyond Humble Point, enlarged by fallen boulders from the Whitlands slip of 1840, is Charton Bay with large grey pebbles at the eastern end. Further west the pebbles are smaller and sometimes there is even sand below the outcrop of Blue Lias. Below the Plateau the remains of the 'Berar', which came aground with 1200 tons of timber in 1896, can still be seen at low tide. A spring, the Gusher, emerges here.

Crumbling White Lias near Humble Point.

A boat provides the best view of the coast.

From the Gusher to the Axe

The westernmost ammonite rich Blue Lias, known as the Slabs, is marked by the remains of the Brixham trawler 'Fairway' which has lain here since 1978 together with a rusting digger which attempted salvage but got stuck. Beyond, much of the faulted cliff base consists of black Triassic fossiliferous shales below grey green mudstones.

Culverhole, an unstable gully full of scrub, plant rich flushes and eroding sand is much changed. In 1804 a lease included 62 acres of meadow and pasture called Culverhole, otherwise called Culverhouse, while a survey of 1525 records the holding of *'one close called Culverhouse Lees which contains 80 acres of pasture'*.

Haven Cliff, the final stretch of richly coloured red brown desert mudstones and grey green silts, is overrun by slurry falls after winter rains. Before 1976 these masked the parent rock but that wet winter exposed the mudstones and by steepening the cliff changed access to the hinterland above, the so called Elephants' Graveyard. The soft cliffs and their seepages provide a specialist habitat which continues above as one turns along the Axe.

Great care must be taken on this walk. Always stay away from the cliffs. Do not try to reach the coast path from the beach. Check the tides before you start.

Cliff spurrey.

Yellow-horned Poppy near the Slabs.

The Mouth of the Axe from Haven Cliff.